To Ailsa.
2019
Lottz of Love
Dad

HAMISH McHAMISH

Susan McMullan is a fast-talking project manager and self-confessed grammar fiend.

Born and raised in Broughty Ferry, she is a graduate of the University of Dundee. She is fluent in French but less au fait with writing about herself in the third person.

Susan is married to a St Andrean and the couple live happily in the Auld Grey Toun with their not-so-famous but much-loved cat, Holly. *Hamish McHamish of St Andrews – Cool Cat About Town* was Susan's first book.

HAMISH McHAMISH

LEGEND OF ST ANDREWS

SUSAN McMULLAN

BLACK & WHITE PUBLISHING

First published 2012
by Black & White Publishing Ltd
29 Ocean Drive, Edinburgh EH6 6JL

1 3 5 7 9 10 8 6 4 2   17 18 19 20

ISBN: 978-1-78530-155-1

Typeset by Creative Link, North Berwick
Printed and bound by Opolgraf, Poland

For my wonderful husband Kevin, for his everlasting love and support

In loving memory of Marianne Baird

A word from Hamish's Mum

Did you know that according to folklore no one can 'own' a cat? The saying recognises the fact that cats are independent free spirits. They may deign to keep you company, accept food and a warm place to sleep, but in the end it's up to them who they choose to view as their rightful owner, if anyone at all.

Hamish was the epitome of Kipling's 'cat that walks by himself', and even when I first brought him home as a tiny kitten, I had to accept his choice of lifestyle! Once he had grown out of kittenhood, he decided my house and garden were far too small for his adventurous nature and he began his wandering ways. His absences from home became longer and longer, until he stopped visiting altogether.

I put up with the empty-nest syndrome for a few years but eventually succumbed to getting a resident dog and then understandably Hamish had a genuine excuse for never coming to visit – he scorned all dogs!

Once a year I had to initiate a search to find him so that I could take him to the vet for his annual health check. Thanks to the good folk of St Andrews, Hamish remained well-fed and healthy, even into old age.

If he could have spoken, I think he wouldn't have said 'I belong to St Andrews', but rather, 'St Andrews belongs to me'!

Marianne Baird, 2012

Introduction

With his fluffy white mane, shaggy ginger coat and big green eyes, it was obvious from the start that Hamish McHamish was no ordinary cat. Streetwise, savvy and fiercely intelligent, Hamish could hold his own in no uncertain terms. He was also hugely affectionate and generous with his time and friendship. With the loudest purr you'd ever heard, Hamish could melt your heart in an instant.

For 17 years, Hamish roamed the streets of St Andrews and lived his life his own way – as a cat about town. He became a local legend and enjoyed an almost celebrity-like status. Adored by St Andreans, students and tourists from all over the world, Hamish brought endless amounts of joy to the good folk of one of Scotland's most historic towns.

Everybody had their own story about Hamish – like the time he casually took on a fully-grown Labrador and won, just because he felt like it; or the moment he walked across the stage at Madras College in the middle of school assembly; the manner in which he simply wandered into any house he liked at any time and the way people just let him because he was Hamish McHamish.

There was an unwritten rule in St Andrews: if Hamish came to visit, you had to let him in. There was even a saying here that a shop could only be considered a true success once Hamish had called to say hello.

The sense of community that Hamish brought to St Andrews was undeniable. One glimpse of his Facebook page shows just how many people were brought together on a daily basis by the town's most famous feline resident. Hamish lifted people's spirits and brightened up the lives of even the most faithful of dog lovers. It's the simple pleasures that keep us all going, and there was something incredibly humbling about an animal that relied on the generosity of strangers to get by. Hamish didn't judge, wasn't fussed if you were rich or poor and didn't mind whether or not you could give Einstein a run for his money. Instead he lived unquestionably on the kindness and collective good of the human spirit.

I originally wrote this book because Hamish was unique and so many people felt that he deserved to be celebrated. The response I had while collecting Hamish's photographs was overwhelming. Everybody was tickled pink that he was to be honoured with his own book at last. Thank you to all those I worked with – you made this book possible, and for that I am ever grateful. I hope this updated version will help the memory of Hamish live on and mean that more people can share in the joy of his story.

One of the other many highlights of writing this book was meeting Hamish's long-lost owner and hearing all her stories including how Hamish actually came to be St Andrews' cat about town. Marianne was a lovely lady, whom I admired greatly and, thanks to Hamish, we became firm friends. She cherished Hamish very much but fully supported him in his wish to roam free. And so he did. Sometimes the handsome chap would stop for her to say hello in passing, but it wasn't long before he was on his way again to see what other adventures the world had to offer.

Marianne wholeheartedly trusted all of the people of St Andrews to take good care of him, just as Hamish trusted them too. She chose Hamish because he was the boldest of the litter, and bold he certainly was.

It was only fitting then that in April 2014 a beautiful bronze statue of Hamish McHamish was unveiled in St Andrews' town centre courtesy of the efforts of Flora Selwyn, founder and editor of the *St Andrews in Focus* magazine. The unveiling sparked global interest and even Hamish joined in the celebrations but he remained decidedly unconvinced by the new guy in town!

His popularity continued to grow and he regularly featured on national and international television and in newspapers. All sorts of marvellous creations were fashioned in his honour – from limited edition Wemyss Ware pottery to artwork, songs and ice sculptures. Admirably, a Foundation was even set-up in his name as an ongoing means of supporting local community improvement projects.

Throughout it all, Hamish remained unphased and carried on as he had always done, with help from the good folk of St Andrews and the dedicated group who took on the responsibility of ensuring of his safety and well-being in the midst of his new-found appeal – something that was particularly important towards the end.

Hamish passed away peacefully in September 2014, following a short illness and with his mum by his side. He had been taken in by a very kind family not long before he became ill but unfortunately the chest infection he had been battling proved too much.

The news evoked an outpouring of love and kind messages from all over the world as people celebrated the life of one of Scotland's favourite felines.

Much to our surprise, it quickly transpired that Hamish was a little older than Marianne had thought and when she received his final documents from the vet it became clear that he was in fact the grand old age of seventeen when he passed away.

Marianne thought long and hard about what to do with his ashes and in the end, she decided that he should have a permanent resting place duly marked. Once I had arranged for a suitable headstone to be made, Marianne chose a nice sunny spot in her garden by the cherry tree and it was there that we laid Hamish to rest.

To this day Hamish is dearly missed by all those who were lucky enough to meet, know and care for him but his memory lives on in St Andrews and beyond, and thanks to his statue it's as if Hamish is still watching over his beloved town.

The perfect tribute to the veritable King of St Andrews, this new edition should be shared and celebrated. So introduce Hamish to your friends and relatives and tell everyone you know about the heart-warming story of the lovable, huggable, wonderful . . . Hamish McHamish. Here's to you, old friend.

Susan Elizabeth McMullan, 2017

This was Hamish
McHamish.
He was no ordinary cat.

You see, he was a very famous cat, and he lived in the ancient town of St Andrews in Scotland.

This is his story.

It all started when he was just a kitten.
Here he was when he was wee — as
cute as cute can be!

Roar! Just like a lion.

Sometimes even lions like to sit in bidets.

Ever since he was
little, he knew he
wanted to roam free.

So one day, he climbed into his mum's fireplace and all the way up the chimney onto the roof. Then he hopped into the tree in his garden . . .

jumped over the wall . . .

And became Hamish McHamish – Legend of St Andrews.
From that moment on, St Andrews belonged to him.

There were lots of things for Hamish to see and do in St Andrews. He spent most of his time roaming around, visiting shops and offices, saying hello to tourists and making new friends...

He liked to visit the students at the University of St Andrews. They called him their study buddy. Did you know that the University of St Andrews is the oldest university in Scotland, and the third oldest in the English-speaking world, just after Oxford and Cambridge? Fancy!

The library was a warm place to go at night.
With all those students working hard, it was
the *purrfect* spot to *paws* for thought.

This was Hamish in St Salvator's Hall, keeping the students company. Sallies is where Prince William first met the Duchess of Cambridge. If the prince had liked cats better than Kates, things could have been so different!

He really was very clever. He even knew how to use zebra crossings.

At student parties he liked to get
dressed up and look the part.

Sometimes the students offered him a wee dram. They should have known that he couldn't drink and meow!

Being a cat about town meant Hamish didn't go home, so he liked to visit his friends for dinner. His Mum didn't mind because she knew that the people of St Andrews were very kind to him and always gave him delicious things to eat.

Like tasty smoked salmon.

And yummy tuna
and chicken.

29

He loved going to this posh
butcher to see what was on
the menu.

He was quite partial to a steak bake or a sausage roll.

At the weekend,
he often went
for a Chinese
takeaway . . .

...or for some Indian food . . .

. . . or for a burger or slice of pizza.
Cattro-formaggi, anyone?

Nothing better than a good
slurp of ice cream on a hot day!

Northpoint
ST ANDREWS

FOOD AND DRINKS
TO TAKE AWAY

...where the POINT is food...

WHERE KATE MET WILLS
(for coffee!)

Wi Fi

Hamish once had a girlfriend called Princess but she stopped talking to him because he kept stealing her food. Maybe he should have brought her here on a date. Looks like a romantic rendezvous.

He sometimes enjoyed a spot of fine dining. This place really should have had a cat flap. Just…couldn't…get…in…

In the mornings he did a bit of yoga.

He liked to get involved and give something back to the community. This was Hamish helping the workmen re-lay the cobbles in Market Street, one of St Andrews' original medieval streets.

Here he was doing a spot of campaigning to help Danielle run for physics president.

On your wavelength...

Danielle for Physics

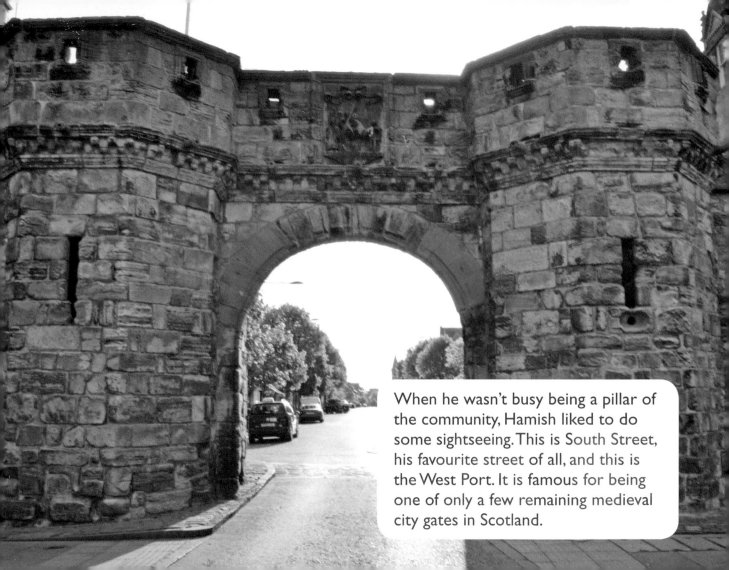

When he wasn't busy being a pillar of the community, Hamish liked to do some sightseeing. This is South Street, his favourite street of all, and this is the West Port. It is famous for being one of only a few remaining medieval city gates in Scotland.

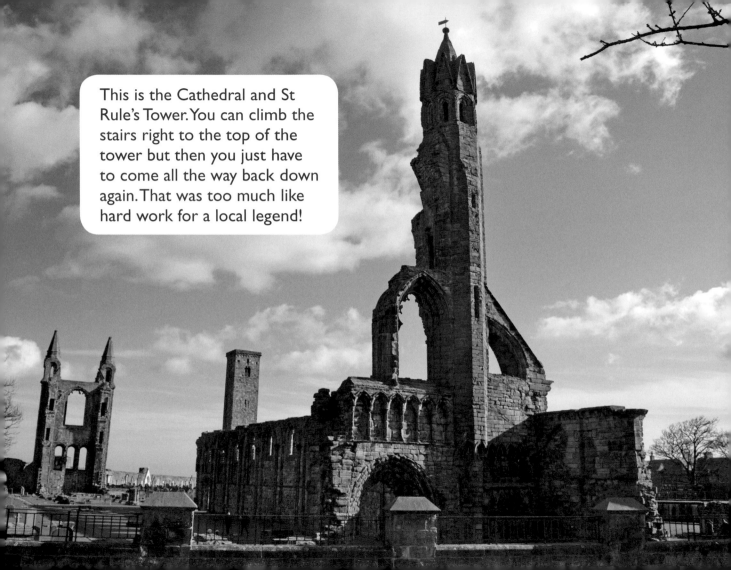

No matter how many times Hamish visited St Andrews Castle, he could never quite muster up the courage to go down into the mines or bottle dungeon. They gave him the heebie-jeebies!

Not far from the Castle is the famous West Sands beach which features in the opening scenes of the film *Chariots of Fire*. Hamish did like to curl up in front of a good movie in the evening...

You can learn all about the history of St Andrews in the town's museums. Maybe one day they'll open an exhibition devoted to the adventures of Hamish McHamish?

Here's a cat's-eye view of St Andrews' pier. On Sundays, students and staff of the University walk along the pier in their red gowns. It's quite a sight, but Hamish wasn't so keen on the salty water.

Hamish liked to watch the weddings in St Salvator's Quadrangle on a sunny day. On North Street, just as you go into the Quad, you'll see the letters PH in the cobbles. It's considered bad luck for students to walk across these letters, and it's said those who do will fail their final exams!

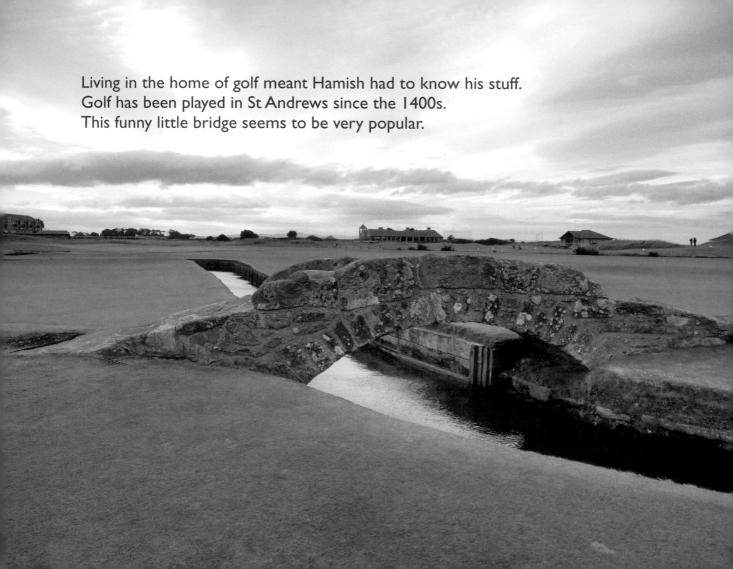

Living in the home of golf meant Hamish had to know his stuff.
Golf has been played in St Andrews since the 1400s.
This funny little bridge seems to be very popular.

This is the world-famous Old Course. It's a curious place where people hit a small white ball with a big stick – with unpredictable results. For cats, it's a very dangerous place. For golfers' egos, it's not that safe either.

Down by the Old Course is Martyrs' Monument. It dates back to 1842 and symbolises the town's role in the Scottish Reformation. Maybe Hamish should have studied *hiss*-tory.

This is the Byre Theatre. It used to be a milking shed for cows. Hamish could have had a lead role in one of their productions. *Puss in Boots* perhaps?

Back in the centre of town you'll find the Whyte-Melville Memorial Fountain that commemorates the novelist George Whyte-Melville.

There are lots of lovely walks in St Andrews. This was Hamish at the Kinness Burn, getting ready for a spot of fishing.

Pooches had to beware – this was Hamish's town! It's a well-known fact that cats are much smarter than dogs. A dog will come to you when called. A cat will take a message and get back to you later.

When he wasn't sightseeing, Hamish liked to call in at all the shops and offices in town. Everybody knew him and looked forward to his visits. Here he was in Waterstones bookshop, one of his favourite places.

He especially liked
the red zappy thing
at the till.

55

These were some of his recommendations for the customers.

Service with a purr!

Being so handsome and so clever was exhausting work!

Let sleeping cats lie. It was important to snooze whenever he could.

Hamish liked to sneak into people's houses to curl up all snug. The good folk of St Andrews didn't mind him popping in for forty winks.

Flowerbeds were comfy too!

Of course, snoozing companions were always welcome.

Le chat s'assit sur le tapis. People from all over the world visit St Andrews, so it was important that Hamish led a cosmopolitan lifestyle. Here he was brushing up on his French.

He made sure he was
well travelled . . .

He learnt new traditions . . .

Here he was in Pretty Things, surrounded by lots of pretty things.

Only £5 in WH Smith – hope they didn't mean Hamish!

Paula and all the other lovely people there made sure he always looked his best.

This was his favourite hairdressers ...

He had his own big red comfy chair in Pagan Osborne, the house shop. The people there were very good to Hamish, especially Pauline and Linda. They washed his blankets by hand because he didn't like fabric softener. He was a very particular cat.

Hamish went to Pagan Osborne every morning. He waited outside until the ladies saw him and opened the door to let him in. If there was nobody at the front door, he knew to wait at the side door.

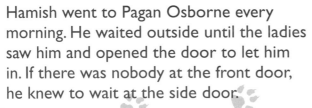

The ladies there let him help them with their work.

At the Association for International Cancer Research offices, Dorothy gave him lots of jobs to do. His paws were a little too big for the computer keys though.

In Moshulu, the shoe shop, he got freshly prepared chicken, cooked to order!

This was one of his favourite chairs in the Sue Ryder charity shop.

Here was Hamish on his mat in the Sue Ryder shop. Cats really do sit on mats.

And this was his other chair. It was a bit small but he could just about squeeze on.

Guest houses were good places to visit. The people in Nethan Guest House were always very welcoming and they served a delicious breakfast.

The people in Aslar Guest House liked Hamish very much too. It wasn't often he smiled for the camera. Over the years he perfected his impassive-as-a-sphinx look which was just right for a cool cat about town.

In Brooksby Guest House the owners knew exactly what he liked for a midday snack — juicy prawns. Here he was next to the Aga in Brooksby in his post-prawn slumber.

Everywhere Hamish went, tourists, students and St Andreans liked to give him lots of hugs and have their photographs taken with him.

Big cuddles!

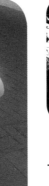

They did some funny poses.

Happy,
handsome
Hamish hugs!

What's new
pussycat?

81

Our very own AristoCat, Hamish McHamish!

Chris Harris wrote:
"A warm summer's day round St Andrews seemed too much for this cat as I turned around to see him on the sofa upstairs in the office at Farmore Interiors. Its owner should consider purchasing the sofa since the cat seems particularly fond of it and no amount of stern talking proved to be enough for it to part from fine taste in fabric."

St Andrews – Home of Hamish

1.

A Hamish Admirer writes:
" A 'dreich' day in St Andrews... Having escaped from the rain, along with many humans – the Sue Ryder shop was rather full – Hamish found that he'd exchanged one trying circumstance for another. Whilst trying to have a quick brush-up and rearrange his damp fur he found some young admirers attentive for rather too long, hence the somewhat discountenanced demeanour!"

2. Lorraine, another admirer, caught Hamish having a brief lie-down in South Street.

A local reader sent in this charming photo and caption:

Badger the Standard Poodle, (a St Andrews resident) is introducing Ashley Kahrs, a visitor from Mountain View, California, to Hamish the town cat who was spotted in Queen's Gardens!

St Andrews
in focus · shopping · eating · events · town/gown · people and more

Even the local magazine, *St Andrews in Focus*, liked to report sightings of him.

I saw Hamish wandering about Madras College recently and wondered if he was looking for an education. Alas, I'd left my camera at home. However.....

Ann Wharmby sent in this charming study. She says that she found Hamish reposing in the Sue Ryder charity shop in Logie's Lane.

Please send in your photos of Hamish, and tell us where you've seen him, and what you know about him.

In fact, some people called Hamish the King of St Andrews.

Hamish
McHamish

Such was the love for Hamish that in April 2014 a beautiful bronze statue of him was unveiled in Logies Lane.

Lots of people came to see the grand
unveiling. There was cake and singing
and bagpipes playing, bringing everyone
in the town together.

Even Hamish joined in the celebrations...but he wasn't convinced by the new guy in town!

Hamish
McHamish

Sadly but peacefully, not long afterwards in September 2014 and at the age of 17, Hamish passed away following a short illness.

To this day Hamish is dearly missed but his statue means he is always watching over the Auld Grey Toun. St Andrews was very important to him – it was his home and its people were his friends.

The next time you visit St Andrews, be sure to take a look around all of Hamish's favourite places. Maybe you'll love this town as much as he did.

Hamish's Credits and Acknowledgements

A thousand thank yous to Emma Haxton for creating Hamish's Facebook page.

Equally big purrs for the wonderful Flora Selwyn, founder and editor of the award-winning magazine *St Andrews in Focus*: www.standrewsinfocus.com.

Sincere thanks and warm wishes to Johanna, Mark and Tristan who provided comfort and shelter for Hamish in his final days.

Exclusive Hamish hugs to all of Hamish's Facebook friends, old and new, who very kindly supplied their photographs for his book. Here are your names on his wall of fame! It's a long list – you might need to put the kettle on.

Adam Moran
AICR St Andrews –
    Dorothy Titterton,
    Suzanne Shaw
Alasdair Johnston
Alex Kekewich
Alexandra Jean Harper
Alexander Mason
Alison Brown
Andrew Jaberoo
Angela Jackson

Anna Kucharska
Anna Moles
Arsa Syed
Ashley Cole
Aslar Guest House –
    Sarah Southall,
    Katherine Palfrey
Barbara McNeilly
Becky Ballantyne
Ben Brown
Bianca Maya Brown

Bradburne & Co –
    Alison Brown
Britt McCray
Brooksby Guest House –
    Caryn Beaton
Caitlin Carty
Catherine Suzanne Barbour
Chendi Hu
Chess Jaconelli
Christopher Impiglia
Courtney Scovel

Dan Labriola
Dainius Macikenas
Danielle Harper
David Bantel
Deirdre Mitchell
Diana Drumm
Dynamic Hair –
    Paula Baker
Eleanor Campbell
Elizabeth Wiebe
Emma Lister

Fiona Don
Francesca Vaghi
Gillian Patterson
Jackie Buist
Jane Rice
Jennifer F. Grant
Jens Munthe
Ka Wing Chan
Kat Scott
Kevin McMullan
Kevin O'Neill
Kirsteen Runcie
Kirstie Read
Klára Žvejklárka
Kristy Ettles
Laura Sneddon
Lauren Allison

Le Rendezvous
Lewis Fairfax
Lisa Crichton
Louise Lane
Lyndsay Mitchell
M Alexandra Bomphray
Madeleine Otto
Maxwell Greenberg
Minick of St Andrews –
    Stuart Minick
Misha Iasinskyi
Morgan Price
Moshulu
Nethan Guest House –
    Rebecca Taylor
    Linzi Taylor
Nicole Judd

Noah Ohringer
Noronha Concepta
Owen Williams
Pagan Osborne –
    Linda Black,
    Pauline Mackenzie-Dodds,
    Neil Fyall,
    Rebecca Richmond
Pamela Davidson
Paraskevi Niki Lampri
Phillip Goose
Pollyanna Delany
Pretty Things –
    Irene J M Harley
Psalm Moatari
Robert Evans
Robert Llyod

Rory Alexander Greig
Shutterstock
Siannie Moodie
Siobhan King
Siti Sabariah
Sophia Nestius-Brown
Stephanie Barrie
Susannah Raymond-Barker
Tanya Bykova
Urte Macikenaite
Wendy Gong
William Staff